THE ART AND
THE WAY OF HARA

THE ART AND
THE WAY OF HARA

SEIGEN YAMAOKA

HEIAN

Heian International, Inc.
P.O. Box 1013
Union City, California 94587

First printing 1976

Revised edition 1992

Printed in Singapore

ISBN: #0-89346-363-9
L.C. Card 76-18413

TABLE OF CONTENTS

†

INTRODUCTION

I recall ever since my childhood my mother saying, "hara ga tatsu" (hara is standing) whenever she became angry. Her statement did not make much sense to me then, but I knew she was angry and that I should not bother her at those times. I also remember once arguing with my father on the finer points of filial piety; he thought I was not showing the proper respect that a well-mannered Japanese son should show his father. The discussion became rather heated, but I did not give an inch in my point of view. Since I was not conducting myself as he wanted, my father chastized me as having a "kuroi hara" (black hara). I was not quite sure what he meant, but I did know he was not pleased with me.

Living with immigrant Japanese parents, I encountered many references to hara. It was not until I went to study in Japan, however, that I realized the meaning of my parents' continued reference to this particular area of their anatomy.

The Japanese way of life focuses on hara. One may even call it their philosophy of life. The way of hara takes in much of the social, physical, and psychologi-

cal life of the Japanese, and it brings them calmness, stability, power, and flexibility. It is also a refreshing, practical, and most natural way of life. The Japanese feel that hara can help not only your everyday life, but that it can be a way to attain the ultimate Enlightenment.

Hara can be translated as "abdomen", "belly", "bowel", "stomach", or even as the American slang term of "gut". It can mean the actual physical stomach, the hypogastric region, or a very special source of power and flexibility known as the "tanden".

The tanden cannot be pinpointed, but is located in the hara region. Although it is a generalized area rather than a specific point, the following methods can be used to locate this area. The tanden is traditionally said to be located some two inches below the navel. One method of locating it is to let all the air out of your lungs by exhaling or yelling; the point of pain deep in the hara is the tanden. The simplest way of locating the tanden, however, is to bend over from the waist. The tanden area is located at the crease.

In this booklet, I will touch on all of these aspects of the word hara, which was introduced to me by my parents long ago.

†

CHAPTER ONE

Views of Hara

We are surrounded by complex and impersonal forces that seem to be beyond our control. If we give in to these forces and allow them to dominate us, our life will just be a cycle of tension, pain, and frustration. We will lose the meaning of life and become robots devoid of feelings and thoughts. We will be alive, but will only exist mechanically.

What we need most is a way by which we can find quiet, peace, and calm within ourselves while in the midst of turmoil. We need a point to focus on which will bring calmness, and through which our total life will be uplifted. We need to find a point within ourselves which will give us mental and physical balance, and at the same time be the source whereby we can experience the ultimate sense of harmony with the universe.

The Japanese refer to that focal point as the *hara*. When we focus on this point, calmness and meaning will be brought into our hectic and often traumatic lives.

The concept of focusing on the *hara* is part of every aspect of Japanese life. Traditionally it was felt that the *hara* housed the spirit of courage, integrity, purity, strength, flexibility, calm, well-being, and meditation.

Because it plays such an important part in the daily life of the Japanese people, the term *hara* is deeply embedded in the Japanese language. It is often used to describe personal characteristics. Some examples are given in the following paragraphs.

It is a compliment to be called *hara no hito*, (a person of *hara*). This does not mean that you have a special *hara*, but that you are a person of courage, will power, strength, determination and character. On the other hand, if you are referred to as *hara ga nai hito*, (a person with no *hara*), you are considered to be a coward and lack determination. In American slang, you would be a person with "no guts" or someone "not having the stomach" for something.

If you were noted as having *hara ga oki*, (a grand *hara*), then people would think of you as being broad-minded, understanding, compassionate, and generous. Conversely, if they said of you, *hara ga chiisai*, (a small *hara*), it would mean you were stingy, small-minded, and cowardly.

It is a compliment when people refer to you as *hara ga kirei* (clean *hara*). You would be considered to be someone with a clear· conscience and very honest. Someone with a *hara ga kuroi* (black *hara*) is dishonest, unfaithful, and untrustworthy.

Japanese often point to their *hara* as a sign of integrity. I have often seen a person point to or pat his *hara*, saying *"makashitoke"*, (leave it to me). He means, of course, for us to place our trust in him—that he will place his *hara* on the line, so to speak.

Reference is also made to *hara* in giving direction. For example, *hara wo kimete*, (determine your *hara*), means that we should clearly define what we are going to do. *Hara wo suete*, (settle the *hara*), means that we should calm down or become settled.

Japanese often express anger by saying, *hara ga tatsu* (*hara* is standing). If a Japanese person had difficulty trying to figure out someone, he would say, *hara ga yome nai*, (can't read his *hara*).

These are only a few examples of how great the extent to which *hara* is used in the Japanese language, and, therefore, how important a part it plays in the everyday life of the Japanese. It is important, moreover, to know that the widespread use of the word *hara* is based on a long tradition of actively developing one's consciousness of this part of the body. How this consciousness is developed is the subject of this book.

In contrast to the Japanese, when an Occidental person talks about the all-important point of the body, he is thinking of the mind or the heart. In the west, it is generally (and possibly romantically) felt that any discussion of courage, stability, balance, strength, and love focuses around either or both of these parts of a person.

I once asked a group of teachers the following question: "Where do you think the source of courage and love is located? That is, if the soul is the focal point of man, where do you think it is located?" Without hesitation, they pointed to either their heart or their head. Even third grade students felt that the heart and mind are more important than *hara*. Their comment was, "You can't do anything with the stomach!"

This sort of reaction is probably due to the strong emphasis placed on the intellect. Occidental people probably point to their heads because they feel it is the source of their intelligence or mental activity. The mind, after all, has the ability to remember, think, desire, calculate, and conceive. Thus it is understandable that it is regarded as the focal point of human life.

However much we may wish to consider the mind as the center of human life, it is also the source of much frustration and turmoil. And it is not entirely able to free itself of its own problems. Much of the tension that we experience daily arises out of our habits of thought. It is a futile activity for us to focus our attention to the mind in an attempt to free ourselves of tension. Attempting to combat tension only leads to further tension; rather than freeing ourselves of tension, we become more deeply embroiled in tension. This is not to say that the mind cannot work out its problems in time, but it is to say that it cannot do so by itself alone.

Other people point to the heart as the center of man, thinking it to be the center of spiritual or emotional living. But this view often confuses spiritual qualities with romantic notions of possessive love, egocentric honor and self-centered courage. Such thinking is rooted in a philosophy of life of being in a state of continual confrontation with the world. Feelings of universal brotherhood, compassion for all of life, and an affirmation of the uniqueness of each living being are not a part of such thinking. No peace and harmony is possible in such romantic idealism, for one is always dominated by the tension of having to prove oneself at all times and against all odds. This, in turn, fosters feelings of self-righteousness and separateness from the rest of life. It is an immature and tense philosophy, and cannot put an end to tension.

The above is not to say that the concept of *hara* does not exist in Western thinking. In Biblical times, it was felt that the "bowels" were the seat of kindness, pity, compassion, and courage. This concept probably evolved into modern slang such as "guts" to indicate courage. However, the concept of "guts" is only a very rudimentary stage of the concept of *hara*, as I shall explain in the following chapters.

†

CHAPTER TWO

The Physical Hara . . . Stomach

Because *hara* is the natural focal point of our well-being, it is only natural that the Japanese have traditionally stressed taking good care of the physical *hara*; that is, the organ known as the stomach. The stomach is a vital part of the entire *hara* area we are discussing.

The stomach is located near the middle of our body. It is an organ in our physical structure that has contact with both the outside world and the inner portion of our body, and thus is a vital center of our health and well-being. The stomach accepts food, slightly broken up by our mouth, and completes the digestive process. As the food is ground and digested, vital nutrients are sent out as energy sources and building blocks for our body. What is considered excess is sent out of the body. When we consider the latter work of the stomach, we can see why romantic notions about the stomach did not develop in the Western world. From a Japanese standpoint, however, elimination is considered quite a natural part of the digestive process.

Since the stomach plays such a vital part in our well-being, it is important to take good care of it. Unfortunately, however, the stomach is one organ that in too many instances is greatly abused.

One way in which we misuse our stomach is through overindulgence. Americans have a tendency to overeat, which causes added work for the stomach. This quite naturally results in indigestion, gas and other discomforts. Continued overeating will cause weight gain and related problems. Overeating can be caused by psychological problems, but generally it is the result of poor eating habits which can be overcome with a little discipline. The uncomfortable feeling after overeating should be considered a warning for more moderation.

Another area we need to consider is the intake of proper foods. Since the stomach sends out nutrients to the entire body, it is important that it be able to have foods which benefit the entire body. Generally we tend to eat what we like, which often turns out to be junk food, and not necessarily what is good for us.

Before going to Japan, my eating habits were very poor. I was a meat-eater with a dislike for vegetables. In Japan I lived in a dormitory where the meals were prepared for me. Since I could not complain about the food set before me, I ate what I was served; the result was a more balanced diet for me. A balanced diet results in a balanced stomach. A side effect was that I began to appreciate the taste of a wide variety of foods rather than just a limited group.

Continuous drinking of cold liquids is not good for your stomach. The Japanese people are generally very careful about this. With all the soda, beer, and other drinks available in this country, we tend to be careless about what we drink. One aspect of stomach care is not drinking a lot of cold liquids before going to sleep. If the stomach should cool off, because we have kicked off the blanket, for example, it is probable that we will have diarrhea in the morning. In Japan it has always been thought that cooling the stomach means poor stomach care.

Since cooling is considered to hurt the stomach, many Japanese wear a *hara maki* (*hara* wrapper) to keep the stomach warm in winter and to protect it from cooling in the summer. The wrappers are usually made of wool. *Figure I* is an illustration of what a *hara maki* looks like.

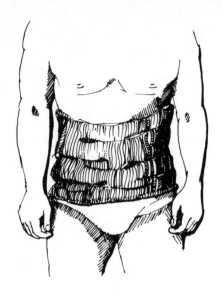

Figure I—Hara Maki

I wore a wrapper all year round during the last four years of my stay in Japan. I didn't believe a wrapper was necessary until my second summer in Japan. Seeing other people wearing wrappers always seemed silly to me, but I soon changed my mind. I began wearing a wrapper because of a terrible experience with diarrhea. At that time I drank a lot of cold liquids before going to bed. Japanese summers are very warm and humid, so I frequently slept without a blanket. The cold from the liquid inside my stomach and the natural cooling from the outside as I slept caused diarrhea. Such cooling of the stomach is not much of a problem in the United States because of central heating, cooling, and the electric blanket.

The Japanese people may seem to be overly concerned about their stomach, but I believe their approach is more correct than ours. The stomach is the center of our physical, mental, and even social well-being. For sound mental, physical and social health, the stomach should be like a finely-tuned violin. When the stomach is over-tuned or under-tuned, problems arise.

If your stomach is in poor condition, your entire physical well-being tends to fall apart. For example, what generally happens if diarrhea causes your stomach to run constantly? There is a dull pain in your *hara* area. You lack energy and power. In short, your body becomes sluggish, dull, listless, and weak. Not only your body, but your mind suffers. Like your body, your mind will be sluggish, dull, and constantly bothered by the condition of the stomach.

Your social relationships will suffer if you are constantly worried about your stomach running or being full of gas. In time, the confidence brought about by good health disappears, as does your social life.

Your stomach is generally the first organ to react to any input into the mind; if your mind is constantly worried about something, your stomach will react negatively in some way. Fear can cause pain or a kind of fluttering sensation known as "butterflies". If stress and tension are acute, they can cause you to go to the bathroom, or if maintained for a long period of time, result in ulcers. Your stomach may be considered as a gauge which reflects all the subtle and irritating influences brought upon your mind. Thus your stomach can be considered to be an indicator of your physical, mental, and social well-being.

This is why you must take good care of your stomach. Proper attitudes must be developed so that you will be able to live in health. This is not to say that your stomach is invulnerable to illness when cared for. It is; yet, vulnerable as it is, since it is the source of our well-being and our point of focus for a better life, we should take the best care of it that we can. This point will be amplified in the coming chapters.

†

CHAPTER THREE

Hara and Physical Activity

Your *hara* is a most important focal point, especially for physical activity. The Japanese have always thought that the well-being of their *hara* determined their physical capability. Consider the following points:

Your *hara* is situated in the middle of your body and is the vital mid-point which balances the upper and lower portions of your body. It is like the center point of a teeter-totter, except, of course, that your body is vertical. Situated at the mid-point, your *hara* is relatively stable and constant in terms of movement and, therefore, it is the center of balance for your entire body.

You may not believe it, but you walk, run, and jump with your *hara* as the point of balance; that is, your body is kept in line with the direction in which your *hara* is moving. I remember a football coach once telling me about open field tackling. He said, "Look at the ball carrier's navel area. He may fake with his head, shoulders, arms, and legs, going every which way to mislead you, but if you keep your eyes on his navel area, you will be able to determine his true direction and make a clean tackle."

Your *hara* has a kind of integrity in balancing your body in that it cannot, in itself, fake anyone out. This is the probable reason the Japanese feel their *hara* is a symbol of integrity.

Another example of the *hara* leading the body is that of a skier going downhill on a bumpy slope. The skier lowers his body to improve his balance. We refer to this as "lowering the center of gravity," but what the skier does by assuming this position is to keep his *hara* in a straight line. The skier's legs may go up and down with every bump he encounters, but each bump is adjusted for by the lowered position of his *hara*. The skier's arms and legs may move in a different direction, but to ski well, the skier's *hara* must be kept relatively stable on the downward course.

Your *hara* area is also that portion of your body which has a natural bend and therefore is the most flexible. Because of this flexibility, we can stoop, sit, twist, lift, and jump. We can bend forward, backward, and from side-to-side without too much trouble. A high diver may make countless corkscrew twists, but his flexibility is stablized by his *hara* area which is able to pull together the upper and lower portions of his body. There is flexibility in the *hara*, and there is also strength.

The *hara* area has a powerful set of muscles. In a relaxed state, the *hara* is vulnerable, but in a contracted state, it is like a brick wall. I have seen a man stand on the *hara* of another man who contracted his muscles in a half sit-up position. Professional prize fighters train by having a heavy medicine ball thrown at their *hara* area. The idea here is to contract the muscles at the moment of impact so they will not be hurt in a fight.

The *hara* area, in itself, is very powerful, but it is also the *source* of power. The power to lift a heavy object actually comes from the *hara*. To lift properly, you must bend your knees and get as low as possible. You must then grasp the object and thrust your *hara* out towards the object you are lifting, keeping your back straight. Lift the object slightly, bring it towards your *hara*, and then proceed to lift with your back straight. By thrusting out your *hara* and keeping your back straight, the lift can be made easily without endangering your back. This method should be used whenever anything is lifted. When lifting something especially heavy, focus on your *hara* by grunting, which will increase concentration in your *hara* and give you the power to lift.

The power of the *hara* is also evident in swinging a baseball bat or a golf club. I have noticed the swings of professional baseball players and golfers. When they swing for power, the power of their *hara* is thrust forward in a straight line rotation at the moment of impact with the ball. The result is a smooth and powerful swing. The focal point of the swing is the *hara*. It is the same with bowling—as the bowler approaches the point of release, his *hara* begins a forward thrust in a straight line towards the head pin. As the ball is released, the follow-through is based on the smooth forward thrust of his *hara*.

Japanese drums (*taiko*) are played with *hara*. The focus on the *hara* is necessary to remove tension from the shoulders, arms, hands, and neck areas. If tension begins to build, the drummer cannot beat the rhythm freely.

The *hara* plays a very important part in singing. We should always sing from our *hara*. Today, the emphasis seems to be more on the throat than anything else. A person who can sing from the *hara* is greatly appreciated in Japan. It is the same in chanting a *sutra* (a Buddhist scripture in Chinese). The reason is quite simple—if we continue to chant or sing from the throat, we will, in all probability, rupture our vocal cords. Control of the sound is not by the cords, but by the power in the *hara*. When this happens, the sound that comes forth is firm, deeply earthy, and vibrant. It is free of the manipulations of the vocal cords. The sound explodes forth as if from the earth itself. This kind of sound is highly regarded in Japanese chanting.

As you can see, *hara* plays an important part in many areas of physical activity. This is why we should take good care of our *hara*.

†

CHAPTER FOUR

Hara and Tension

I have often marveled at how easily the Japanese
seem to endure the tension and pressures of their
society. A sense of calm always seems to prevail. I
believe the way of the *hara* plays an important part
in relieving both the mental and physical tensions of
the Japanese.

Relief from tension is very important, for if tension is not released, it can cause great harm to your
physical and mental well-being. Tension can build
inside us to such an extent that the slightest outside
pressure can cause tremendous damage. In this case,
the body and mind are like a balloon filled with too
much air—even the slightest prick will cause an explo-
sion.

So far I have discussed how the *hara* is viewed, the
importance of the physical *hara*, and *hara* in relation

to physical activity. I wanted to give you some idea of the importance of *hara* in your life. Now, I would like to give some practical applications on how to overcome mental and physical tension with *hara*. First I will introduce an exercise in the use of the *hara*; it will show you the power of your *hara*. This exercise will help your circulation, relaxation, and exercise the physical *hara*, but my primary purpose in introducing this exercise now is to demonstrate how your *hara* works in reducing tension.

Getting Acquainted with Hara

Sit on a chair or on the floor. Hold both your hands up around face level and clench your fists as tightly as possible. Continue by tightening all the muscles in your neck, shoulders, arms, and fists. (*Figure II*) When you start to shake with tension, focus on your *hara*. This is accomplished by forcing power into that area. You should feel a pushing out in your *hara*. Within a few moments, a strange thing will take place. With focus on your *hara*, your *hara* will begin to draw into itself the tension in your neck, shoulders, arms and fists. You will feel the strange sensation of the tension gradually leaving those areas. As you continue to focus on your *hara*, those portions of your body previously full of tension will slowly

22

relax. Not only that, but your mental concentration will also be drawn into your *hara*. Your muscles will relax, and your mind will become calm. Try this exercise a number of times.

Figure II

This exercise should demonstrate to you that your *hara* has the power to relieve mental tension and stress. Let me give an example:

At one time or another, we are all caught in the binds of tension. We know we must do something, but end up doing nothing. Sometimes tension arises when we have too many things to think about.

When your mind is in a state of constant stress and tension, your neck and shoulder areas become tense. To relieve the tension in these areas, you rotate your neck or swing your arms, but what about your mind? Your mind is very active, and it also needs a way to relieve itself of tension—a place where it can send the energy that it has accumulated. More tension is usually created if we try to use "will power" to clear our mind. The reason for this is quite simple; your mind cannot clear itself. Mental tension merely creates additional tension; the tense mind becomes even more tense about its own tenseness! It is as futile as a dog chasing its tail in endless circles of frustration. Try as you may to free your mind, you will find that your mind cannot free itself by itself. If tension is allowed to continue, it can affect even your physical stomach, resulting in poor physical health and lessened mental activity. If your mind is unable to relieve itself of its own pressure, it too can give out.

Before your mind gets into such a drastic state of tension and pressure, it is important that you sit down and focus on your *hara*. If you do so, your mental pressure will naturally drain into your *hara*, freeing your mind and easing your tension. The result is a welcome sense of relaxation and calm.

You may feel that focusing on your *hara* at a time of stress may harm your physical stomach, but there is nothing to worry about. Your stomach is harmed only if you let the tension stay in your mind and let your stomach react to that tension. If your mind is free of tension, then there will be no stress on your stomach.

Unless you are extremely tired, the state of calm that will be attained will not cause you to be less alert in the sense of becoming dull and sleepy. In fact, just the opposite will normally result. Being free, your mind will be more alert, perceptive, attentive, and clear. Your mind will be able to see, hear, and understand what is important. A mind full of tension cannot do this because it is too cluttered.

If you are nervous, focusing on your *hara* will help a great deal. In time of extreme nervousness, we unconsciously take deep breaths to relieve tension. What this does is to cause us to focus on our *hara*. That is, the power to breathe is dependent on our *hara* cavity pushing the air out of our lungs. This is one way of focusing on the *hara*.

When we become tense, it is very helpful to engage in physical activity to relieve the tension. Physical activity helps because it also forces us to focus on our *hara*. However we are not always in a position to do physical exercise. From a mental standpoint, therefore, it is very important to practice focusing on your *hara* by breathing exercises or tightening the *hara* area until it becomes a natural part of your daily mental activity.

Extreme tension can cause us to lose sleep, making us more tense. Because of lack of sleep, we become exhausted, but cannot relax or sleep. Some people recommend counting sheep when we cannot sleep. The idea is that if we concentrate on the dullness of counting sheep, we would fall asleep from boredom. But if we are having difficulty sleeping because of tension, it is probable that we will have difficulty counting sheep. Furthermore, counting sheep is a mental activity which means that we are trying to overcome mental activity by using mental activity, a most difficult process.

An Experiment to Demonstrate the Value of Hara

To give you an idea as to how the *hara* can help, try the following experiment. It requires the help of a partner. Stand so your side (either side) faces your partner. Place your forearm on your partner's shoulder with your elbow facing the floor. Have your partner place his hands, one from each side, above your elbow area and lock his fingers (*Figure III*).

In the first demonstration, remain in this position, clench your fist as tightly as possible, and put as much power and tension into your arm, shoulder, and neck as possible. While you are in that state of utmost tension, have your partner pull down on your arm and attempt to bend it. Because of the tension in your arm, however, and the fact that your partner is using his two arms against your one, the pressure brought to bear on your arm causes tremendous pain, and your arm will bend after a short struggle.

Next, take the same position. This time, however, keep your palm open. Hold your arm semi-rigid to keep it straight, but do not put any tension into your arm. Focus on your *hara*. Imagine that the energy of your *hara* is flowing up and out through your fingers. Now have your partner exert the same pressure on your arm as before. You will be surprised to discover

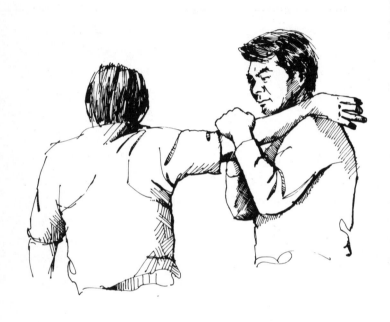

Figure III

28

that try as he may, he will be unable to bend your arm. It is possible to resist because there is no tension in your arm, and therefore no pain, even though tremendous pressure is being exerted.

From this we can see the reasons for outbursts of anger and hate. They are expressions of tension exploding because of pressures brought to bear on us. To be free from angry outbursts, you must have inner calm.

Try this experiment. It will demonstrate vividly the importance of relieving tension and the necessity of focusing on the *hara*.

†

I will now present three ways of using your *hara*. First is breathing from your *hara*, second is by way of physical tension, and the third is a combination of the first two. The idea behind these three methods is to relieve the tension in your mind and spread that energy throughout your body. When you do this, there will be no concentration of tension anywhere.

Breathing From Your Hara—First Exercise

Lie on your back. Inhale slowly and deeply through your nostrils. As your lungs become filled, feel your diaphram go out; this will cause your *hara* to expand. At the peak of your intake, thrust out your *hara* to inhale even more air. Then slowly begin to exhale through your mouth. Towards the end of your exhaling cycle, contract your *hara* muscles to force out the last bit of air. Repeat this process. Breathe between three and four times a minute. Continue this about five or ten times as needed and then return to normal breathing. Since the focal point is your *hara*, your mind will become free of any tension. A feeling of relaxation will be felt and, in time, sleep will come naturally.

Tension Relaxation—Second Exercise

The second exercise may be termed a tension-relaxation process. This exercise can be used in more serious cases of mental tension.

Lie down as before and focus on your *hara*. Tighten your *hara*, and then gradually the entire upper portion of your body. Next, tense the lower portion of your body, starting from your toes and working up. When your entire body is in a state of acute tension, push out your *hara*. Slowly exhale and feel the tension going into your *hara*. It may not seem possible that your *hara*, which began the whole tension process, can be pushed out, but it can. It is possible because your *hara* is extremely flexible. Repeat this process as needed, but not over five times. If done properly, five times will be sufficient to disperse all the tension in your mind. During this exercise, your mind will be free of any thoughts, and as you repeat it, your body will become relaxed and sleep will come naturally.

Third Exercise

The third exercise is a combination of the breathing and tension-relaxation exercises. Begin with the breathing exercise. As you come to the point of completely exhaling, inhale slightly and begin the tension process by putting power into your *hara*. After thrusting out your *hara* and exhaling, slowly start the deep breathing process.

By alternating each exercise three or four times, you will feel a sense of relaxation. The combined process will help to relieve both mental and physical tension.

Alternating tension and relaxation is conducive to sleep, but it is also good general exercise for the body. It will help your circulation, muscle tone, and is one way of exercising your stomach for better health.

†

CHAPTER FIVE

A Man of Hara

What kind of person lives by *hara*? Who is a man of *hara*? I touched lightly on these areas already, but let me go into this in a little more detail.

Anyone can live by *hara*. You do not have to be any special kind of person. All it takes is an understanding of *hara* in your life and to utilize the great and vast potential of *hara* for your own physical, mental and social benefit. It will take discipline to be sure, but is there anything worthwhile that does not?

A man of *hara* is a person who lives the life of *hara* in every aspect of his life. This way of life gives him confidence, direction, a sense of responsibility, meaning, and an awareness of the things in the world about him. Such a man will not claim he is a man of *hara*. The distinction, "man of *hara*" is given to him by others as a natural outgrowth of respect and admiration. Those he has helped or who have come in contact with him refer to him in such a manner. That others refer to him in such a way is not always known by the individual himself. It is the highest tribute to the character and quality of the man that the Japanese can express.

I would like to tell you about a person whom I feel is a man of *hara*. I met Kenju Masuyama when he was President of Ryukoku University in Kyoto, Japan. I had heard much about him before I met him. He served as professor at Ryukoku University, Bishop of the Buddhist Churches of America, President of Kyoto Women's University, as a scholar of the Jodo Shinshu Hompa Hongwanji Temple, and in numerous other important capacities.

As chief administrator of the University, he was very busy, but he always had time to help students who needed it. He was not a prolific speaker or conversationalist, but when he spoke, he did so with authority and compassion. He was a tremendous listener. He often grasped the problem before you finished explaining.

At that time, I was a scholarship student of the Buddhist Churches of America, which has headquarters in San Francisco. After completing work on my Master's Degree at Ryukoku University, the BCA headquarters requested that I return to the United States to start my ministry. Although I had completed my academic requirements, I felt I was not spiritually ready to start my ministry, and I wrote about my feelings to the headquarters. The reply I received was that I had to return. With much uncertainty, I went to see President Masuyama. He nodded when I entered his office, motioned me to sit down, and then motioned me to begin. I explained my problem and he listened. From time to time he would punctuate my remarks with an "un" which indicated he was listening. I must have rambled on and on, repeating myself several times, but he did not interrupt me. After I finished, he said he understood, and that was that. I said thank you and left his office.

President Masuyama did not say anything to indicate that he would help me, but somehow I knew he would. I did not know how he would go about it, however. As far as the subject was concerned, it was closed and nothing was said after that. I continued my education an additional three years, but I did not receive any further reminders about returning to the United States. Only after returning to the United States did I learn what happened. Soon after our conversation, President Masuyama personally wrote to the Bishop of the BCA and requested that I be permitted to stay in Japan and further my studies. He said that if need be, he would take personal responsibility, and it was for this reason I was permitted to stay and continue my studies.

Many people have been helped by President Masuyama in the same quiet and unobtrusive way that I was, and I feel that many consider him a "man of *hara*". I certainly do.

But how does a person become a "man of *hara*"? Is the *hara* actually involved? We tend to say a person becomes a man of *hara* because he has acquired understanding through education, has come through difficult periods in life, or that he is knowledgeable in the area of human feelings. These things are important, but can easily become deterents because you can become arrogant with *only* these qualities. In order to become a man of *hara*, I believe the most important factor is the *hara*.

The general description of a man of *hara* is someone with courage, will power, strength, determination, character, integrity, honesty, and patience. Such a person is also known as a person with a "big *hara*", that is, he is generous, compassionate, and understanding.

I feel the key factor that makes the difference is how a person focuses on his *hara*. A man of *hara* is noted for his ability to listen, take hold of the problems of others, and give direction.

How well do we listen to others? Don't we form conclusions even while someone is talking, even before he is finished? Don't we tend to interrupt others to get our so-called two cents worth in? Aren't we so busy thinking of what *we* want to say that we are not really listening? Our minds move a mile a minute, centering on ourselves rather than the person we are supposedly listening to.

A man of *hara* is different. As he listens, he focuses on his *hara*. His own thoughts and possible conclusions are drawn into his *hara* and neutralized, so to speak, leaving his mind free. He does not interrupt except possibly to ask for a clarification. He lets the speaker talk it out. He is patient and nods or gives some sign that he is listening, but he takes it all in without any blockage from his own mind. In other words, if I may express it this way, he listens with his *hara*.

Digesting all that was said, a man of *hara* generally gives clear and precise answers. He can give direction, because he has heard the entire problem. At times, he will help the speaker solve his own problem. He subjectively feels what the speaker is feeling, but he is also objectively regarding the speaker, and so is able to guide and help. If he himself must do something to help, he will; once it is done, however, the incident is forgotten. There is no thought of obligation or returning a favor in the actions of a man of *hara*.

We can often work out the problems of others, but have difficulty solving our own. This is because our emotions prevent us from seeing our own problems objectively. But when a man of *hara* faces a problem, he focuses on his *hara* and clears his mind of any one-sided thoughts before his mind gets too emotional. When he does, he is enabled to visualize the problem from his *hara*, a perspective greater than himself, and thereby determine his own course of action objectively. At times, he will focus on his *hara* after experiencing all the emotional aspects of his problem. Whichever course he takes, his actions are generally characterized by respect, patience, and responsibility.

A man of *hara* is respected by others because of his ability to help others, but also because he is able to responsibly work out his own problems.

Although it is not easy to become a man of *hara*, everyone has the potentiality of becoming one. The key is whether we can focus on our *hara* or not.

†

CHAPTER SIX

Hara and the Martial Arts

The martial arts (*budo*) place great emphasis on the *hara*. I believe the word "*do*", used in the names of martial arts such as Ju*do*, Ken*do*, Karate*do*, and Aiki*do*, which means "way", is really the Way of *hara*. In the martial arts, the *hara* is the source of power, balance, speed, flexibility, and that all-important source of "no-mind" (*mushin*).

From my experience I feel that Karate stresses the way of *hara*. The art of Karate is really the art of making the mind and body one. The mental and physical discipline of Karate can bring about the realization of oneness involving all that one *IS* as a person. The entire method of practice of Karate as an art is created to advance the student to the ultimate awareness of his being. This awareness is made possible through the *hara*.

The first thing a Karate student learns is the relationship of his body and *hara*. The first stance I learned was the straddle-leg stance. In this stance, (shown in *Figure IV*), the feet are firmly placed on the floor with the toes of both feet pointing forward. The legs are spread about twice the width of the shoulders; the knees are bent outward. This stance is somewhat like sitting in a saddle. I was told to keep my back straight and alternately tense and relax the muscles of my legs and hip area. In order to tense the area, I had to thrust my *hara* forward. This was my first serious and practical introduction to *hara*. When I began to practice moving techniques, I was constantly reprimanded for putting too much effort in my shoulders or for letting my legs drag.

"Move with the *hara*" was a constant admonition by my instructors, and to prove their point, they pushed me this way and that to show that I did not have proper balance and control. As speed and coordination entered into my movement, I gradually came to feel what it meant to move with *hara*. If I did not, I would lose my balance, stability, speed, and power. My *hara* was not only my center of gravity, but also my source of reflex and power. I found that if I focused power on any other part of my body, I could easily be thrown off balance. The following

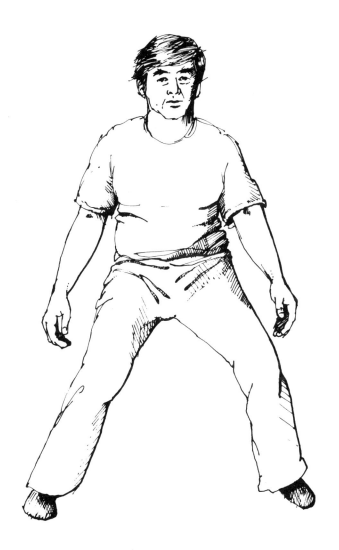

Figure IV—Straddle-leg Stance

exercise will help you become aware of your *hara.*

Becoming Aware of Hara

Take a moderate straddle-leg stance with knees straight. Put power in the upper portion of your body and start to bend backwards. Before going too far, you will find yourself losing balance. At that point, swing your arms about to regain balance. Before you know it, you will fall over backwards.

Next, in the same stance, keep the upper portion of your body loose and relaxed. Let your arms hand naturally at your side. Focus on your *hara* by putting power into that area and lean backwards. You will find yourself in control even though you bend twice as far back as before. In that position, start swinging your arms about. You will find yourself going backwards again. When we find ourselves falling backwards, we often scream and swing our arms about in hopes of regaining our balance. However, that only places power in the upper portion of our body, and, as a result, we fall most of the time. As you feel yourself going over, if you relax the upper portion of your body and focus on your *hara*, chances are you will be able to regain your balance.

I found that the *hara* is a strong stabilizing factor in offensive and defensive Karate movements.

Experiencing the Stabilizing Strength of Hara

The following exercise will give you some indication of the great stabilizing strength of the *hara*. It requires a partner.

Stand with your feet about shoulder width apart. Move one leg straight forward about twice the width of your shoulders. Bend the front knee, keeping the back straight, and fully extend the rear leg. Have your partner take a position in front of you, but in the opposite stance (see *Figure V*). Have him hold your belt. In this position, first tense the entire upper portion of your body and have your partner lift. He will be able to do so with ease. Now put power in your *hara* and the lower portion of your body. Be sure the upper portion of your body is in a relaxed state. Have your partner try to lift you again. If you do this correctly, your partner will be unable to do so. This is the ultimate strength of the *hara*.

In Karate training, you must focus on your *hara*, both physically and mentally. That moment of focus must be instantaneous, natural, and without mental contrivance. That is, your body and mind must become one with your *hara*, in free reflex motion.

While your body is learning to move with your *hara*, your mind will have a battle all its own. Your

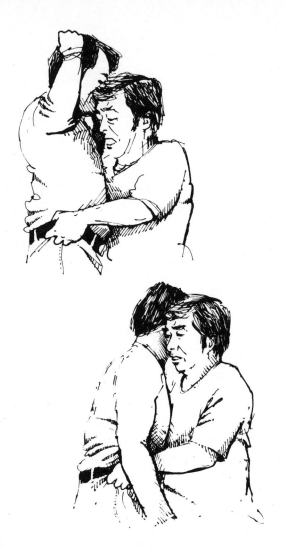

Figure V

mind will be caught up in such problems as muscle ache, monotony of practice, ranking, fear, fatigue, victory, defeat, and patience . . . Focusing your mind on *hara* is not easy under such circumstances.

In practice, I found my mind constantly cluttered with thoughts. My body functioned well, but my mental attitude was poor. The next step for me was to become aware of the "no-mind" that is emphasized so much in Karate.

Experiencing "No-Mind"

I first experienced "no-mind" when I was delegated to break a brick with my fist for a demonstration. Since it was my first attempt, a practice session was held first. The first time you see the brick you are supposed to break, you wonder if you can break it or if it will break your hand. While watched and encouraged by my instructors, I set up the brick and took my stance. As I prepared to strike for the first time, my mind was full of thoughts such as "Can I really do this?", "Will it hurt?", or "Will I ruin my hands?"

As I began my strike, I sensed a fear of pain somewhere in the back of my mind. That caused me to involuntarily tighten my arm. Because of that momentary uncertainty, I lacked the power and speed to break the brick. I will never forget the pain when my fist first made contact with the brick. I was all for giving up then and there, but I was told to try again. My hand hurt and was beginning to swell, but the instructor paid no attention to this. He said, "This time, yell (*kiai*). Don't think about the pain. If you break the brick, it won't hurt at all."

I took my stance again and looked at the brick. I could not help wondering what was going to happen to my fist. I inhaled some air and with a yell, attacked the brick. In that brief moment, there was no thought of the brick, my fist, or the pain. In the emptiness of that moment, my fist met with the brick and when I looked, the brick was broken. With the "*kiai*", my mind focused on my *hara*, and the power and the speed to break the brick was freely and naturally manifested from my *hara*. In that moment, my mind was free of any thoughts, and through my *hara*, became one with my body; it was a moment of "no-mind".

We are constantly reminded to focus on and move with *hara* within the highly regulated training method of Karate. That moment of focus must be free and natural. When a Karateka confronts himself, defeats himself, and becomes one with himself, it can be said that his mind and body are one with itself in "no-mind". In this point of oneness through the *hara*, the Karateka is calm and reflective like water. He is free from victory or defeat, self or opponent, life or death; he has fulfilled the meaning of his art. Reflected in the calmness of his mind through *hara*, the Karateka moves naturally and relfects the movement of his opponent. Such a person is a master of Karate.

But it does not end there. On a personal level, the Karateka should also reflect in the calmness of his mind through *hara*, the natural being of all things and life. He should move naturally in the harmonious situation of his life in total relationship with everything else. He should feel the wisdom of interdependence and interrelationship as it is reflected in his mind through *hara*, and feel the infinite compassion, warmth, and gratitude for that total reflective relationship. Realizing this, the Karateka will not use his art to harm or hurt others. Karate is only a means to attain the awareness that all things and their natures are one. When you attain this level, the art of Karate ceases to be. There is only the serene life of gratitude and non-violence in the truth of interdependence.

Hara in Other Martial Arts

The importance of *hara* can be found in other martial arts as well. In Judo, *hara* is the point of balance, stability, speed and power. I have often seen a Judoka in a good position to throw his opponent, but who could not budge his opponent. What the opponent did was to yell and place his power in his *hara*, thereby grounding himself to the mat. If, on the other hand, the opponent had his power in his arms, shoulders, or if his mind was filled with thoughts, then he would have been thrown with ease.

It is important to move with *hara* in Kendo. The balance of the sword depends on the balance achieved through *hara*. Also, the stroke of the sword with only the arms is not effective or powerful enough. Only when the stroke is in tune with the power of the *hara* is it clean and accurate.

In Aikido, the point of reference or focus is the *hara* area where the *ki* (source of power) is located. In the circular and soft movements of Aikido, it is essential that you focus on "*ki*". Grace, flexibility, balance, and power all come from the "*ki*".

In each of the above martial arts, unity of body and mind is essential. Everything works towards this end in training. This is why I believe that the "*do*" or "way" in the martial arts is really the way of *hara*. We can thus see why the term *"do"* is also used in *Bushido*, or the Way of the Samurai. The training and purpose of the Samurai is much the same as in the martial arts in general. It is difficult to state definately whether the Samurai used to perform *Seppuku* (disembowelment) by slashing open his *hara* because the *hara* was the source of ultimate personhood. However, we cannot discount this fact or possibility either. If the *hara* is considered the source of the Samurai's ultimate personhood, then we can understand why the act of disembowelment was considered the ultimate act of courage and integrity.

The word *"do"* is also used in other cultural arts such as *Sado* (Art of Tea Ceremony), *Kado* (Art of Flower Arrangement), *Shodo* (Art of Calligraphy), and others. In order to achieve the ultimate of an Oriental art, there must be unity of body, mind and object in harmonious oneness. This should indicate to you how important *hara* is in these arts as well.

†

CHAPTER SEVEN

Hara and Meditation

Meditation is a very important part of the cultural, social and personal life of the Japanese. The results of meditation can be seen in the refined naturalness of brushwriting, flower arrangement, tea ceremony, and the martial arts. The results of meditation are due to rigid and firmly-defined methods of practice. The practice method is so rigid that it consumes us, but in the end, it is what sets us free. I believe that the way of *hara* is the key meditative practice.

In my opinion, *hara* greatly influenced the Japanese meditative tradition. I base this opinion at least in part on the general use of the word *hara* in everyday life by the Japanese people. For example, one is told to think things through by "settling the *hara*" (*hara wo suete*). If you cannot decide on a course of life, you are told to "determine your *hara*" (*hara wo kimete*). Such common expressions naturally express the importance of *hara* for the Japanese. In the past, I am sure the references to *hara* meant to focus on the *hara* in a serious meditative manner. These phrases probably developed from the Buddhist practice of meditation. The meaning of *hara* has drastically changed since then to what is now a popular expression to give direction to life. What is important, however, is the clear indication of how important the *hara* is as a point of reference for serious meditation.

Before we get to the point where we use *hara* in meditation, however, problems will be encountered. After the point of *hara* has been attained, other problems will arise. Some of the problem areas for serious meditation are given in the following paragraphs.

The first major problem is our reluctance to really start meditation. Many of us believe that meditation is not important. We are caught up in the rat-race of life so that we do not have the time nor do we feel we can afford to make the time to meditate. In fact, we make every excuse for not doing so. Then again, some of us do not want to talk about the subject because it is so different from what we are used to, or because of fear. We fear to stop running. We fear the quiet and silence which brings with it thoughts that we do not want to think. We fear the stillness. We may discuss the importance of finding peace of mind, but we are not willing to work for it. This is a contradiction to be sure, but these are our real feelings. This is the first hurdle we must pass.

A second major problem arises because we do not really know what meditation is or how to go about it. What do we do when we meditate? The following is a method of meditation:

Find a quiet place and sit for about fifteen or twenty minutes, preferably morning and evening. If all you can manage is once a day, however, that is fine. You may sit in a chair, but the best way is to sit on the floor in the lotus position, a half-lotus, cross-legged, or legs underneath (*seiza*). The half-lotus position is illustrated in *Figure VI*. In the first three positions, using a pillow to elevate the buttock area will be helpful. Keep the back straight, shoulders comfortably back, arms relaxed, neck and the back of the head in a straight line with the back, and hands resting comfortably on your lap.

In this position, focus on your *hara*. Concentrate on breathing from the pit of your *hara*. You do this by slowly and deeply inhaling. Follow the air going down to the pit of your *hara* with your mind, and then follow the air out. As you do this, you will find that in order to concentrate on the air at the pit of

Figure VI—Half-lotus Position

your *hara* and with the power in your *hara*, your mind becomes empty. There is a natural shift of focus from the mind to *hara*, *hara* to mind, and so on. Do this a few times and then return to normal breathing.

Your breathing will become shallow, but continue the meditation. The important thing is to perform this exercise daily. If you do, the time will come when you experience a tremendous sense of calm.

It takes time, concentration, patience and endurance to meditate. Many give up before achieving any results. Because this practice is so relaxing, we may stop at this point in the meditative process and do it only for the purpose of relaxation. But you must persist in order to be introduced to the *hara*.

If you continue, the next problem to arise will be that your mind has difficulty in concentrating and giving itself up to your *hara* while breathing deeply. Your point of focus will tend to remain with your mind instead of going from one to the other. Your mind will begin to wonder if the point of focus is more on itself than with your *hara*. Your mind will probably take over at that point. If it does, things begin to happen. Some examples are: Time becomes an enemy. The question, "How much longer?" creeps into one's mind. This brings a sense of frustration, impatience, awareness of discomfort, and even a sense of futility. The quiet and the silence will become deadening. Then such thoughts as, "It's a waste of time," "I'm too busy for this kind of stupid thing," "I have better things to do," "I'm not getting anywhere" will fill your mind. Many stop at this point.

If you persist, however, the next problem to arise is answering the question, "Is it a waste of time?" Your mind will find itself going in all sorts of directions—reading books, talking to teachers, trying to emulate the experience of others, or trying to put the meditative quest out of your mind altogether. Instead of bringing peace and calm, meditation becomes the cause of inner turmoil. From time to time the turmoil within you will strike out by demeaning others or by going on the ego-trip of "Look at what I am doing." This only results in further aggravation for ourselves. As your problems and frustrations grow and accumulate, your mind will find itself so stuffed and cluttered that it will not know what is what. In time, your mind will find itself drifting into the sphere of not knowing anything. But it is precisely then that your mind naturally takes refuge in the *hara*. In that refuge, your mind frees itself, and yet it is free to come back to itself. It is here that your *hara* gives your mind the refuge to free itself, and yet gives your mind capacity to know beyond itself.

The key is discipline and practice. The interesting thing is that what is attained, though grounded in discipline and practice, is free from discipline and practice at the point of *hara*.

This is one example of what can happen in the serious practice of meditation. Because of the complexity of the problems involved, it is best to meditate under a master or a teacher who can guide you at every point along the way. Because the way is different for each of us, the keen eye of a master will mean the difference between success or failure for you.

One day I saw a man sitting before a statue of Amida Buddha. He was sitting in the *seiza* position, comfortably erect, with hands together in *gassho*. From somewhere deep within him, the sound of *Namu Amida Butsu* (uttering the Name of Amida Buddha) came forth in a continuous stream of "*Namandabu*". The sound was earthy, vibrant, and full of warmth. He seemed to be free from any thoughts. Yet as free as he was in his recitation, he was grounded to the mat upon which he sat. He appeared sturdy, immovable, centered, and one with everything around him. As I sat and watched, I could not help but think, "Here is a man of Faith (*Shinjin*). A man who is the result of disciplined practice." I believe he was a man of *hara*.

This type of meditative discipline can be found in the training of all Japanese cultural traditions. In the

57

tea ceremony, there is the discipline and practice of folding the cloth, washing the bowl, and serving the tea. In flower arrangement, there is the continuous placing of flowers in the vase to reach the point of free expression in a disciplined form. In brush writing, there is the going over and over of one stroke to perfect it so you can write that one stroke without any hinderances. In the martial arts, there is the continuous process of doing the same movements over and over again until you reach the point of peace and calm "reflective like water".

In each tradition, the student follows the instruction of the master or teacher until he can cut the cord of that relationship and the cord that binds himself to himself.

The final point to be made about meditation is that although *hara* plays an important part, you can become attached to it, in which case *hara* becomes a crutch and a hinderance. In the final analysis, you must become free even of *hara*.

†

CHAPTER EIGHT

Enlightenment Through the Hara

In Western man's search for meaning, the emphasis has been placed on his mind or intellect because the mind is thought to be the source of ability, greatness, compassion, feeling, and courage. But though the mind is the source of our answer for meaning, it is also the source of our frustration in finding meaning. The question is, "How does man solve this contradiction within his own mind?"

I feel that *hara* can play a vital part in solving this contradiction.

Buddhism teaches the Middle Way where duality merges into oneness. This teaching encourages a way by which extremes are avoided. A problem arises however, when we rely on the mind in order to understand this teaching.

It is our mind that separates and divides our problems into many diverse segments, resulting in duality rather than oneness. We often find ourselves in extreme situations because our minds are set on what we want or do not want. In conversation, for example, it is common for our minds to tune out the other person's point of view and concentrate on our own point of view. When the mind alone is used to engage in lofty intellectual discussion, philosophical positions can be taken as to what life is or is not, or even arguments about how many angels can dance on the head of a needle.

There is also the problem of ego-attachment. Once it becomes active, the mind has a difficult time letting go of itself. The mind can become so attached to itself that it will do anything to maintain its superior position. The great fear of an ego-attached mind is no-mind or simply non-ego because to the ego, non-ego means the total annihilation of its existence. Other concepts such as self and desire work in a similar manner.

It is our mind that brings out the questions which challenge our resolve in tackling a difficult problem. For example, in the midst of a difficult situation, how often does the question, "Is it worth it?" come forth? In other words, our minds often discourage our endeavors with thoughts such as "It's not worth it." We discourage ourselves with negative thinking, doubt and fear.

Our lives are pulled apart with the duality caused by our minds. We are taught to do one thing and we make every effort to follow through, yet our mind, working through our ego, desire, and such, seeks to benefit only itself. We work against our own best interests. This is why the Buddha said that we are the result of what we think. This is why we are frustrated, full of stress and tension, and uncertain regarding the course and meaning of life. We are off balance. Our focus is wrong. It is strange that when we concentrate, we often sit down. Perhaps this is an unconscious attempt to gain some balance. I believe we sit to ground ourselves. I believe sitting is an unconscious attempt to focus on our *hara*.

I have seen many statues of meditative Buddhas in the sitting position. Their faces are gentle, relaxed and compassionate-looking. The shoulder areas are also relaxed with no sign of tension. The *hara* protrudes, but with the feeling of total focus in that area. The legs in the lotus position are firmly grounded. The impression that I had was that through the *hara*, the Buddhas depicted are all one with the universe. At the same time, they manifest to the world the wisdom and compassion that they have attained. They were firmly grounded and yet free.

Let us consider Enlightenment through *hara*. There are as many ways in which you can attain the Buddhist experience of Enlightenment as there are individuals. No one person's experience is the same as for another. Because of his uniqueness, each individual must experience his own way. The ways of others only point in a general direction. But regardless of which direction that experience manifests itself in, I believe *hara* plays a very important part. Three examples are given below.

A Zen koan is a question which is incapable of logical analysis and is given by a master to boggle the mind of a student. Mentally, in meditation, the student tries to analyze the question and come up with an answer. The situation is intensified as he goes to his master and finds his solutions constantly rejected. His mind is full of thoughts, but every avenue through which he seeks an answer is blocked by his master in rebuke. As time goes on, he begins to hate his master for the torment he is going through. But this does not help at all. In time, the student finds he cannot think, does not want to think, but is afraid not to think. At this point, he can do one of two things: slide back or go forward. It is easy to slide back because his mind is constantly suggesting this possibility. It is difficult to go forward because of the conflict in his mind. If he chooses to go forward, the student will find himself with a single purpose and resolve. All his thinking is focused upon himself and his mind. He is by himself in the lonely battle of fighting himself. The strain of finding a solution, self-pity, egotism and ignorance all mill about in his mind. His mind is so full it has no place to go. When it is about ready to explode with exhaustion and exasperation, from deep down comes the automatic focus on breathing. At that moment, the tension and stress brought about by his mind desperately clinging to the limitedness of its own self-preservation is given up to the *hara*. In that instant, his mind becomes free. The tension draining into his *hara* frees the student's mind to see beyond itself. The universe, in total relationship, floods into his free mind. Tension and turmoil are released, but more important, the contradictions and dualism that previously existed freely and naturally merge from one to many and from many to one. Joy encompasses the student who ecstatically runs to his master, and his master, seeing that his student is no longer a student, rejoices with a fellow follower of the way.

A second example: A priest related the following personal experience to me. "I made it a daily practice to recite the sacred name, *Namu Amida Butsu*, before Amida Buddha. I did this because I felt I understood the teachings. It was my way of expressing gratitude.

"One day, due to a severe sore throat, a sense of helplessness and frustration came over me when I sat before Amida Buddha, because I could not recite His Name. The frustration grew because I felt the need to recite, the need to fulfill my duty, the need of feeling the assurance and security of hearing myself recite.

"The more I tried to recite and found myself unable to, however, the more frustrated I became. I felt useless; my identity was at stake. In desperation, I began to repeat *'Namandabu'* in my mind. It seemed to work at first, but then I had difficulty concentrating. Other thoughts came into my mind.

"I then recalled a teacher once saying *'Namandabu'* comes from the *hara*. I thought about this and tried to apply it. It became an obsession with me and even after my voice returned, I continued trying to recite from my *hara*. One day, as I tried to concentrate on my voiceless recitation, I noticed that *'Namandabu'* was not centered in my mind. Rather it seemed to be located just below my vocal cords. It was a strange feeling. I felt a temporary sense of exhilaration and peace, but it did not last. I tried to recapture that feeling, but I could not. Frustration and tension mounted. Then, as I attempted to concentrate, I automatically took a deep breath and exhaled. At that moment, *'Namandabu'* exploded in the pit of my *hara* and burst forth in a voiceless recitation which shook my entire being. I felt an overwhelming sense of freedom, peace, harmony, oneness, and gratitude in the resounding silence of that explosive moment. My being, mind, and the universe seemingly came together in warmth, love, peace, calm, and compassion. It is a difficult thing to describe."

A third example: A man is told that he is powerless and cannot attain Enlightenment through his own efforts, that Enlightenment is assured only by the Compassion of Amida Buddha. But because this man's ego will not let him admit such a thought, he rejects this teaching. If he is powerless, he thinks his mind, self, ego, knowledge, and such, mean nothing, and he is nothing. He rationalizes by saying that the self is important, and that if it is not, he is as good as dead. He searches for Amida Buddha with these thoughts in his mind. He tries to find Amida in his heart, but Amida is as illusive as a ghost and just as unreal. A teacher poses a question to him, "How can a self-centered person like you find Amida? You cannot even utter the Name of Amida."

The contradiction of what he seeks and what he is pulls him poles apart. Try as he may to pull them together, he finds himself further and further from what he seeks. Anger, frustration, and hatred fill his mind. He tries many things in order to forget, but he cannot. He is up against the wall of himself, seeing himself, with no escape from himself. A sense of isolation, emptiness, and aloneness grips him. He sees his ego at work and desperately wants to accept himself as a being of ego, yet cannot. To accept means that his ideal of himself crumbles to nothingness. There is no escape but to accept. Then, from the pit of his *hara* a sound rushes forward. The sound can come out as *"kwatz!"* or an unintelligible sound, or a yell which signifies the total realization of insignificance. The sound, coming from the deep pit of his *hara*, explodes into the world. There is no hanging on. The first wave rushes forth with others to follow, but in time subsides, leaving his body limp, exhausted, tired, but strangely relaxed and free. At that point, he visualizes the past, present, and future as an endless stream. In this stream, as an egotistical fool, he demanded that the world owed him his due, when in reality, he owed the world a great debt which he can never repay, a debt which continues to grow as long as his life exists and even beyond. He sees all that must be in order for him to be. It is a being that in ignorance he previously denied. In timeless time, the weight of life lifts and wells into meaning, gratitude, responsibility, and a touch of humility. Tension is gone. He realizes it was all due to the Compassion of Amida Buddha. There is an endless stream of *Namu Amida Butsu.*

As subtle as these examples may be, the pit of our being is our *hara*. It is when our mind, naturally and without contrivance, focuses on our *hara* that the self and the body become one. This is not an easy thing to do. Practice is necessary for your mind to naturally focus on your *hara*. In the beginning, your mind must constantly focus on it. This can be done through breathing exercises or the practice of thrusting out your *hara* from time to time. Your mind is still in control at this stage, however, because it is what causes focusing on your *hara*. With practice, however, focusing on your *hara* becomes a natural function and will be done without thought or contrivance.

In Buddhism and particularly the Jodo-Shinshu tradition of that teaching, much is said about the concepts of ego and self. In the examples above, we see the tremendous conflict in the individual because of the two. Ego or self, within our being, causes great turmoil because of fear for its own existence. It is caught in attachment to itself. The ego or self can totally dominate the individual's mind. But if the focus is on the *hara*, the ego and self are diffused into the flow of the *hara*, and into the Universe to which they originally belong. The ego and the self thus become non-ego and non-self. In such a state, there is totality, wholeness, or oneness. There is the realization of uniqueness and wholeness. The reason for this is that we realize the unique causal conditions which make us individuals, yet we are not separate from the causal conditions of the universe which sustain us. We are a part of it and therefore flow within it, free from the contradiction of the previous self-centered ignorances, egos, and selves. The inner tension becomes part of the flowing energy of the universe itself, but it is free.

Experiencing Oneness with the Universe

Sit in a *seiza* position (legs underneath). Fill your mind with thoughts and tense the muscles in your shoulder and neck. Next, have someone stand behind you, place his hands on both sides around your hip area, and push. He will be able to slide you across the floor very easily. If he should push around your shoulder area, you will fall over.

Next, while you are in the same position, remove all tension from your shoulders and neck. Relax your arms. In other words, relax the upper portion of the body. Focus on your *hara*. As you focus on your *hara*, your mind will become empty naturally. Ask your partner to push from behind as before. This time he will not be able to slide you across the floor. You will be firm, rigid, but relaxed. Most important, you will be in balance.

What happens is that your mind sends the energy that it has to the *hara*. The *hara* takes in the energy, thus causing the relaxed state and focuses it downward. This is why you seem to be glued to the floor; that is, you are one with the floor. If you are one with the floor, then it naturally follows that you are also one with all that is one with the floor. Going further, you are one with that upon which the floor is grounded, that is, the earth itself. Going further still, you are also one with everything that is on the ground, that is, the trees, flowers, mountains, rivers, and so on. This being the case, then you are also one with all those things that give life and meaning to those things on the ground; the rain, sky, clouds, sun, moon, and stars. In short, you are one with the universe and all that is in and beyond it. You are one in total relationship. This is Enlightenment through *hara*.

Conversely, the universe or Enlightenment can come into us at the point of *hara* where the mind is free from any contrivance. In Jodo Shinshu, it is at the point of *hara* that Amida Buddha's Wisdom and Compassion awakens the "no-doubt mind" of *Shinjin* in us. Then, from the point of *Shinjin*, the joyful and grateful utterance of the name of Enlightenment is expressed through our mouth as *Namu Amida Butsu.*

In this Enlightenment and *Shinjin*, there is the wisdom to see things as they are, but with a profound sense of responsibility, gratitude and compassion for those inter-relationships that we have.

Hara is the power source of our being. It is the source which makes the flow of that which is natural possible. It resolves all contradictions; it is our source of oneness to which we originally belonged.

CHAPTER NINE

The Art of Hara (Haragei)

In most aspects of communication in Japan, Hara is used as a focal point. This is known as the "Art of Hara". To the Western mind, the idea of communicating with the Hara must seem improbable. Yet, in most important meetings, the Japanese use the Art of Hara to work out problems in communication.

It is critical to understand that the person who uses the Art of Hara approaches any meeting with a sense of open possibilities. In other words, he is working within a space which considers the entire relationship. Therefore, there is no beginning or end, no affirmation or negation, and no horizontal or vertical in the discussions. The person using Hara begins with a clean white canvas on which there exist no marks of limitation. This is the starting point for communication when the Art of Hara is used.

When working with people of Hara, it is often difficult to fathom what they are thinking, and it is easy to misinterpret their responses. I've encountered this problem many times, and I'm sure that many people in the world of business have also run into this strange wall of open space. Let me recount my experiences in working with a university in Japan.

With my totally Western mindset that is the result of having been born and educated in the United States, I approached a Japanese university to ask for help in raising funds in Japan. I was privileged to meet with the important department heads of the university to make my presentation. During this presentation, I occasionally received nods of affirmation as well as questions which, at the time, did not seem appropriate. But for the most part my audience remained silent, all the while taking copious notes in Japanese.

Upon conclusion of my presentation, I asked for any responses. There was silence. (Silence is crucial in Hara communications, because it provides an opportunity to expand base assumptions.) Flustered, I started to rattle on. My audience listened and then praised me politely for my hard work. The President of the university stated that the plan was good. At this point I was elated. I felt that I had succeeded in my presentation and that I would get their support. At the party which was later held in my honor, I felt even more confident of success because none of the officials indicated otherwise.

I returned home expecting to hear immediate messages of support or word regarding development of the plan. I heard nothing. Why? In retrospect, I realized that to the Japanese, my presentation covered but a small portion of the spacious canvas that was my fund-raising project. It was not complete. True, they had praised me for my work, but that praise was for working so hard to make the presentation. It was not a comment on their approval or acceptance of the project. My presentation was not inclusive enough; hence, there was no praise forthcoming in that regard.

I travelled to Japan a number of times after that. Each time, I filled in a little more of the canvas. And I learned that the nods and questions from my audience were not meaningless—rather, they pointed to areas that needed to be worked on and developed. Although my frustration grew, I was also forced to reconsider and expand my thinking. In the process, my presentation became more rounded, and there developed a grudging mutual respect on both sides. Eventually, my presentation developed into a plan which accounted for the inter-relationship of both parties.

As these parts fell into place, I noticed a shift in the entire process. I had done my best, and my project now had to stand on its own merits. In a sense, I became free of the project. And strangely enough, I found myself experiencing the Art of Hara!

Now that they were able to see the major portion of the canvas covered and the potential byproducts that could evolve from this project, the university officials actively began to express their points of view. At first they pointed out only the weak links and the negatives. I took a deep breath, nodded, and remained silent. In time, however, the negatives became conciliatory statements aimed at strengthening the weak areas. I received sound advice and encouragement. The discussion was frank and to the point—what is known as "Hara wo watte". The end result was mutual cooperation and a clear sense of responsibility for all concerned. We had finally reached a consensus that was workable and beneficial for all involved.

It took three years to reach that point. Why did it take so long? I believe it was because, initially, I stated only my position. I took a self-serving linear approach which did not consider the total space that we all needed. I was asking for their participation, but only on *my* terms.

In the Western world where we value the intellectual approach, we are taught to speak our minds. Many things are determined, based upon the power of our persuasive skills. We seek a quick response in which "Yes" and "No" are clearly articulated. In the Art of Hara, however, there is no clear-cut answer in the beginning—only a blank canvas that is gradually filled through spatial discussions of shared concerns (with each side presenting their ideas), eventually leading to a mutually satisfactory conclusion. To do otherwise is divisive and not beneficial for the whole.

The Art of Hara is not unique to the Eastern mind. If we look deep within ourselves, we too will find that space within that can help us to master the Art of Hara.

A friend once described a discussion that she had with her father. All that her father said went against her grain. She perceived the discussion as "him against me". As her father kept talking, she shouted in desperation, "You're not listening!" But he persisted. Tired of arguing, she decided to listen and not say a word. She took a deep breath and sighed as she struggled to control her impulse to interrupt and continue to argue. Without knowing what she was doing, she had actually pushed the impulse down to her Hara. Soon she began to listen- and she was able to hear, for the first time, what was really being said. After listening to all her father had to say, she calmly related her side of the issue. This resulted in mutual understanding. In short, my friend experienced the Art of Hara.

We have the opportunity to cultivate the Art of Hara in every aspect of our lives because it is a natural part of our lives. Hara is the source of our mental, physical and social balance; it is the original point of our inner balance and stability. Somehow, we lose Hara during our growth to adulthood.

For modern man, the search for inner balance is even more complex due to the automated lifestyle that surrounds him. This lifestyle takes him even farther away from the original point of his own inner balance, and people spend billions of dollars each year in search of it.

Scientists, inventors, motivators and doctors have developed, and are still developing, a variety of methods for uncovering the primal source of our strength, inner balance and calm. However, that source has never really left us—it has been with us from the day that we were born, and it is still with us even at this moment. Our problem lies in the fact that we have lost touch with it in the maze of our lives and in the misguided concept that our quest for inner calm must be answered from a point "outside" of ourselves. Sadly, we think that we must find that source of peace "out there" and then try to bring it "into" ourselves. This concept poses a very serious question: "If there is turmoil within, can the calm 'out there' really affect us?" After all, it has always been said, "Calm can only come to those who are calm within." Therefore, in order to achieve that calmness, it is necessary to first discover the natural calm that lies within us.

Once upon a time, the Hara was that natural source of calm and balance for all of us. Let us consider the infant, for example. The infant does not have the muscular development to grasp things with any power. Their arms are very flabby. However, if you have ever had an infant take hold of one of your fingers, you no doubt noticed that the infant was capable of tremendous power. It is a kind of relaxed strength, and if you observe the infant closely, you will see that this power comes from a source other than hand or arm muscles. The infant naturally focuses on the Hara—in other words, strength is manifested from the Hara. That is why there is no tension in the infant's arm or shoulder.

Even when an infant cries in anger or joy, his vocal power comes from concentration at the point of Hara. When he first begins to lift his head or crawl, again the point of focus is clearly the Hara. A friend who watched her little niece trying to stand for the first time reported that the child's concentration on balance was so intense that she was totally centered for this effort. When she managed to stand, the child squealed in glee and clapped her hands, thus breaking her concentration on her natural center point of focus, the Hara. She immediately plopped back down on her seat.

However, the focus on Hara becomes less and less emphasized as adult mannerisms are learned during the growth process. This natural point of balance is neglected, and we eventually forget about this natural center of inner balance and calm. But as adults, we once again begin to search for this point of balance within ourselves—the point that was once so natural.

Living by Hara is a natural process that is free of any contrivances. We can see it in the infant, and our task is to try to return to that inner balance of Hara. In order to do so, we must rediscover that part of our selves that we used so freely at one time in our lives—that part that we "grew" out of to become the limited persons that we are. We must learn how to grow and live by Hara, becoming fundamentally expansive natural beings. In so doing we can rediscover this natural and original point of inner balance and calm, and we will have achieved the Art of Hara.

BIBLIOGRAPHY

Anesaki, Masaharu. *History of Japanese Religion.* Tokyo: Charles E. Tuttle Company, 1963.

Buddha, Truth, and Brotherhood. Japan: The Federation of All Young Buddhist Association of Japan Publication, 1934.

Castile, Rand. *The Way of Tea.* New York: Weatherhill, 1971.

Conze, Edward. *Buddhist Meditation.* New York: Harper and Row Publishers, 1956.

Draeger, Donn F. *Modern Bujutsu and Budo.* New York: Weatherhill, 1974.

Durckheim, Karlfried. *Hara with the Vital Centre of Man.* London: George Allen and Unwin Ltd., 1962.

Haguri, Gyodo. *The Awareness of Self.* Yokohama: General Printing Co., Ltd., 1967.

Herrigel, Eugene. *Zen in the Art of Archery.* New York: Pantheon Books, 1970.

Inagaki, Zuiken. *Tannisho no Shinzui.* Kyoto: Hyakkaen, 1961.

Jodo Shinshu. Kyoto: Otani University, 1961.

Joya, Mock. *Things Japanese.* Tokyo: Tokyo News Service Ltd., 1960.

Kaibara, Ekiken. *Yojokun—Japanese Secret of Good Health.* Tokyo: Tokuma Shoten Publishing Co., 1974.

Miyamoto, Musashi. *Gorinsho.* Tokyo: Tokuma Shoten, 1963.

Moore, Charles A., ed. *The Japanese Mind—Essentials of Japanese Philosophy and Culture.* Honolulu: East-West Center Press, University of Hawaii, 1967.

Nakayama, Masatoshi. *Dynamic Karate.* Tokyo: Kodansha International Ltd., 1966.

Nishiyama, Hidetaka, and Brown, Richard. *Karate: The Art of "Empty Hand" Fighting.* Tokyo: Charles E. Tuttle Co., 1960.

Omori, Sogen. *Sho to Zen.* Tokyo: Shunjusha, 1973.

Ratti, Oscar, and Westbrook, Adele. *Secrets of the Samurai.* Rutland: Charles E. Tuttle Co., 1973.

Suzuki, Daisetz T. *Zen Buddhism.* New York: Doubleday and Company, 1956.

———. *Zen and Japanese Culture.* New York: Bollingen Foundation, Inc., 1970.

Takakusu, Junjiro. *Essentials of Buddhist Philosophy.* Hawaii: University of Hawaii, 1949.

Thera, Nyanaponika. *The Heart of Buddhist Meditation.* New York: Samuel Weiser, 1973.

Tsunoda, Shodo; Masunaga, Shoko; and Kumata, Kenryo. *Buddhism and Jodo Shinshu.* San Francisco: Buddhist Churches of America Publication, 1955.

Watanabe, Jiichi, and Avakian, Lindy. *The Secrets of Jodo.*
Vermont: Charles E. Tuttle Co., 1960.

Westbrook, Adele, and Ratti, Oscar. *Aikido and the Dynamic
Sphere.* Tokyo: Charles E. Tuttle Co., 1970.

INDEX